COMMON CORE CLINICS

Grade 5

Mathematics

Number and Operations–Fractions

Common Core Clinics, Mathematics, Number and Operations–Fractions, Grade 5
OT321 / 413NA

ISBN: 978-0-7836-8495-6

Author: Rebecca Motil
With special thanks to mathematics consultants:
Debra Harley, Director of Math/Science K–12, East Meadow School District
Allan Brimer, Math Specialist, New Visions School, Freeport School District
Cover Image: © gthompsonphotography/Veer

Triumph Learning® 136 Madison Avenue, 7th Floor, New York, NY 10016

Printed in the United States of America.
10 9 8 7 6 5 4 3

ALL ABOUT YOUR BOOK

COMMON CORE CLINICS MATH will help you with key concepts.

A **Key Words** box introduces new math words. An **Example** shows you how to solve problems in the lesson.

Each lesson has **Guided Practice**. Hints called **THINK** and **REMEMBER** help you work through the problem.

There are two pages of **Independent Practice** with problems for you to solve on your own. You will also solve some **Word Problems**.

At the back of your book, there is a **Glossary** and **Math Tools** that will help you work out problems.

Module 2 Number and Operations–Fractions

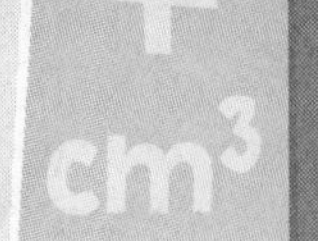

1 Equivalent Fractions

Key Words

equivalent fractions
fraction

A **fraction** names part of a whole or a group. Fractions that name the same amount are called **equivalent fractions**. You can use number lines to find equivalent fractions.

You can also use multiplication or division to find equivalent fractions. Just multiply or divide the numerator and denominator by the same number. Multiplying or dividing the numerator and denominator by the same number is the same as multiplying or dividing by 1, so the value of the fraction is unchanged.

Example 1

Find a fraction equivalent to $\frac{3}{4}$.

Use the number lines. Find a fraction that is the same distance from 0 as $\frac{3}{4}$.

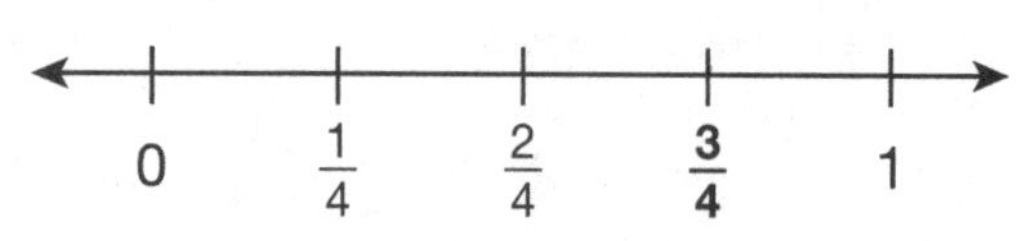

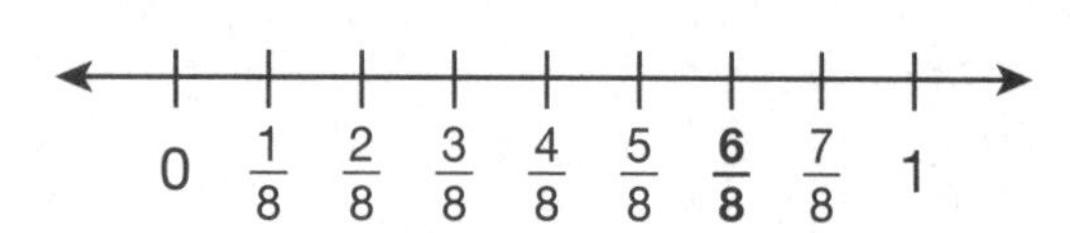

$\frac{6}{8}$ is equivalent to $\frac{3}{4}$.

Example 2

Find a fraction equivalent to $\frac{1}{2}$.

Multiply the numerator and denominator by the same number.

$$\frac{1}{2} = \frac{1 \times 3}{2 \times 3} = \frac{3}{6}$$

$\frac{3}{6}$ is equivalent to $\frac{1}{2}$.

APPLY

Find at least two other fractions equivalent to $\frac{1}{2}$. Explain how you know.

Guided Practice

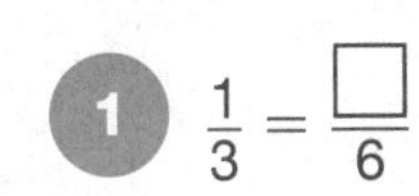

1 $\frac{1}{3} = \frac{\square}{6}$

Step 1 Use the number lines. Circle the fraction that is the same distance from 0 as $\frac{1}{3}$.

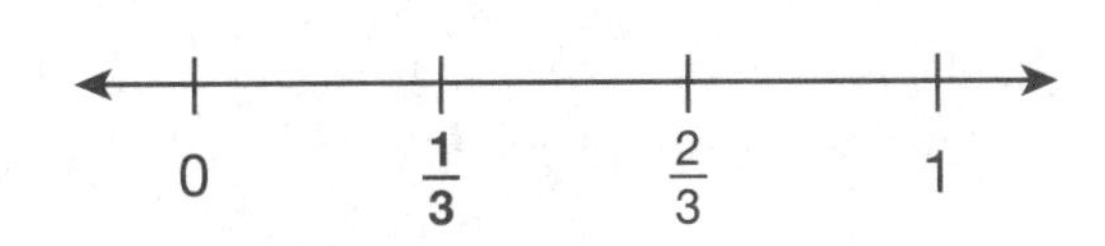

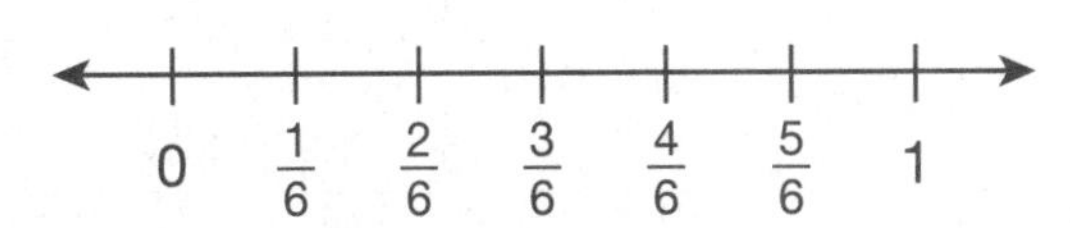

REMEMBER
Equivalent fractions are the same distance from 0 on a number line.

Step 2 Write the numerator of the equivalent fraction.

$\frac{1}{3}$ is equivalent to $\frac{\square}{6}$.

$\frac{1}{3} = \frac{\square}{6}$

2 Find two fractions equivalent to $\frac{4}{6}$.

Step 1 Multiply the numerator and denominator by the same number.

$\frac{4}{6} = \frac{4 \times 2}{6 \times 2} = \frac{\square}{12}$

Step 2 Divide the numerator and denominator by the same number.

$\frac{4}{6} = \frac{4 \div 2}{6 \div 2} = \frac{\square}{3}$

THINK
Multiplying or dividing the numerator and denominator by the same number is like multiplying or dividing by 1.
$\frac{2}{2} = 1$

________ and ________ are equivalent to $\frac{4}{6}$.

Independent Practice

1. How can you use number lines to find equivalent fractions?

____

____

2. How can you use multiplication or division to find equivalent fractions?

____

____

Use the number lines to find equivalent fractions. Write the numerator.

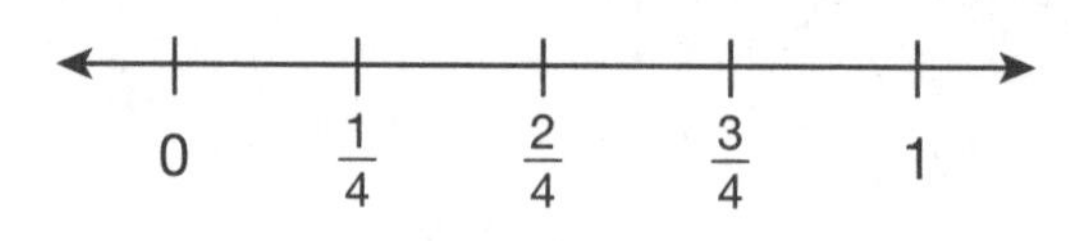

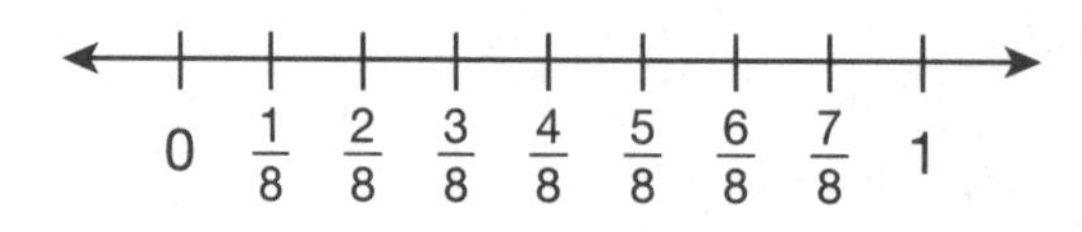

3. $\frac{1}{4} = \frac{\square}{8}$

4. $\frac{3}{4} = \frac{\square}{8}$

5. $\frac{4}{8} = \frac{\square}{4}$

Use multiplication to find an equivalent fraction. Write the numerator or denominator.

6. $\frac{1}{5} = \frac{\square}{10}$

7. $\frac{3}{8} = \frac{\square}{16}$

8. $\frac{2}{3} = \frac{6}{\square}$

9. For a recipe, Andre needs $\frac{1}{2}$-cup butter. The butter comes in $\frac{1}{4}$-cup sticks. How many $\frac{1}{4}$-cup sticks of butter does he need?

____

Use multiplication to find an equivalent fraction.

10. $\frac{1}{3}$ = ________

11. $\frac{3}{6}$ = ________

12. $\frac{2}{5}$ = ________

13. $\frac{3}{5}$ = ________

14. $\frac{2}{7}$ = ________

15. $\frac{3}{4}$ = ________

16. $\frac{7}{8}$ = ________

17. $\frac{3}{7}$ = ________

18. $\frac{5}{6}$ = ________

Use division to find an equivalent fraction.

19. $\frac{8}{10}$ = ________

20. $\frac{6}{12}$ = ________

21. $\frac{8}{12}$ = ________

22. $\frac{2}{14}$ = ________

23. $\frac{5}{15}$ = ________

24. $\frac{2}{10}$ = ________

25. $\frac{10}{15}$ = ________

26. $\frac{8}{16}$ = ________

27. $\frac{5}{20}$ = ________

Solve each problem.

Sun-Hee cut a sandwich into sixths. She ate $\frac{1}{3}$ of the slices.

28. How much of the sandwich is left in sixths?

____

29. How much of the sandwich is left in thirds?

____

2 Improper Fractions and Mixed Numbers

Key Words

mixed number
improper fraction

A **mixed number** is made up of a whole-number part and a fraction part. A mixed number can be written as an **improper fraction**, where the numerator is greater than the denominator.

Look at the fraction model.

Each rectangle is divided into 5 parts. That is the denominator. 7 parts are shaded. That is the numerator.

$1\frac{2}{5} = \frac{7}{5}$

Example 1

Write $2\frac{3}{8}$ as an improper fraction.

Write a fraction for the whole number. Use the denominator, 8.

$$2\frac{3}{8} = \frac{2 \times 8}{1 \times 8} + \frac{3}{8} = \frac{16}{8} + \frac{3}{8}$$

Find the sum of the fractions.

$$2\frac{3}{8} = \frac{16}{8} + \frac{3}{8} = \frac{19}{8}$$

$2\frac{3}{8} = \frac{19}{8}$

Example 2

Write $\frac{9}{4}$ as a mixed number.

Divide the numerator by the denominator.

$9 \div 4 = 2 \text{ R1}$

Write the mixed number.

$2\frac{1}{4}$ The quotient, 2, is the whole-number part. The remainder, 1, is the numerator. The denominator, 4, stays the same.

$\frac{9}{4} = 2\frac{1}{4}$

GENERALIZE

How can you tell if a fraction is greater than 1? How can you tell if a fraction is less than 1?

Guided Practice

1 Write $1\frac{5}{6}$ as an improper fraction.

Step 1 Write a fraction for the whole number by using the denominator, 6.

$$1\frac{5}{6} = \frac{1 \times 6}{1 \times 6} + \frac{5}{6}$$

$$= \frac{6}{6} + \frac{5}{6}$$

Step 2 Find the sum of the fractions.

$$\frac{6}{6} + \frac{5}{6} = \frac{\square}{6}$$

$1\frac{5}{6}$ = __________

REMEMBER
When adding two fractions, add the numerators only. The denominators stay the same.

2 Write $\frac{14}{4}$ as a mixed number in simplest form.

Step 1 Divide the numerator by the denominator.

$14 \div 4 = 3 \text{ R}2$

Step 2 Write the mixed number.

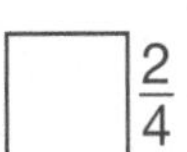

THINK
The quotient, 3, is the whole-number part.
The remainder, 2, is the numerator.
The denominator, 4, stays the same.

Step 3 Write the answer in simplest form.
A fraction is in simplest form when the numerator and denominator have 1 as their only common factor.

$$\frac{2 \div 2}{4 \div 2} = \frac{\square}{\square}$$

In simplest form, $\frac{14}{4}$ = __________.

THINK
To write $\frac{2}{4}$ in simplest form, divide the numerator and denominator by the same number, 2.

Independent Practice

1. Explain how to write $2\frac{1}{4}$ as an improper fraction.

____

____

2. How can you write any improper fraction as a mixed number?

____

____

Write a mixed number and an improper fraction for each.

3. 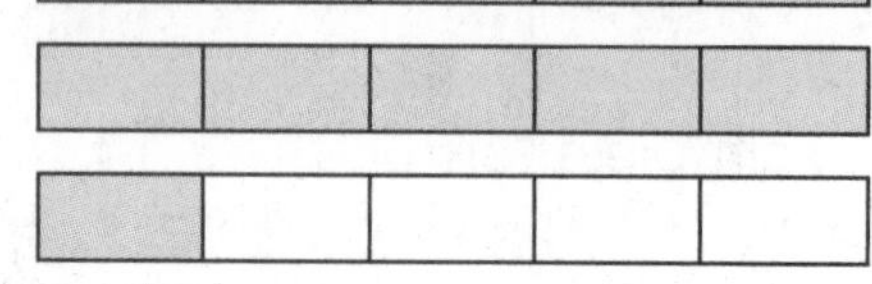

____

4. 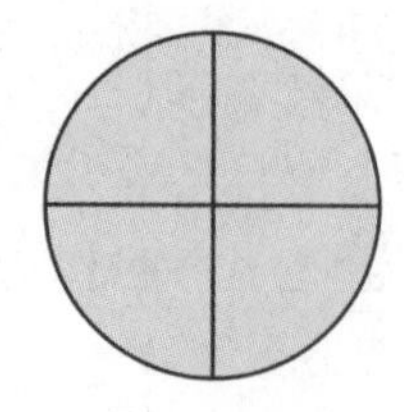 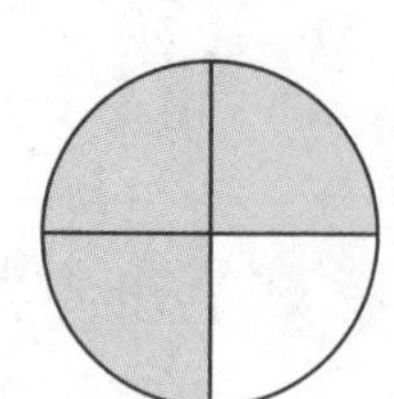

____

Write as an improper fraction.

5. $1\frac{5}{8} = \frac{\square}{8}$

6. $2\frac{1}{3} = \frac{\square}{3}$

Write as a mixed number.

7. $\frac{12}{5} = \square\frac{\square}{5}$

8. $\frac{19}{6} = \square\frac{\square}{6}$

9. Sofia used $2\frac{1}{2}$ cups of flour to bake a cake. Write the cups of flour she used as an improper fraction.

____

Write as an improper fraction in simplest form.

10. $1\frac{2}{3}$ = ________

11. $3\frac{2}{6}$ = ________

12. $4\frac{3}{10}$ = ________

13. $2\frac{4}{8}$ = ________

14. $7\frac{1}{3}$ = ________

15. $5\frac{2}{5}$ = ________

Write as a mixed number or a whole number in simplest form.

16. $\frac{10}{8}$ = ________

17. $\frac{9}{6}$ = ________

18. $\frac{15}{4}$ = ________

19. $\frac{14}{10}$ = ________

20. $\frac{18}{12}$ = ________

21. $\frac{40}{10}$ = ________

Solve each problem.

22. Chloe walked $\frac{25}{15}$ miles to the library. Write the distance that Chloe walked to the library as a mixed number in simplest form.

____

23. Dion needs $1\frac{1}{2}$ cups of flour for a recipe, but he only has a $\frac{1}{4}$-cup measuring cup. How many $\frac{1}{4}$ cups of flour does he need to make $1\frac{1}{2}$ cups? Explain.

____

____

3 Add and Subtract Like Fractions

Key Words

like fractions

Like fractions have the same denominator. For example, $\frac{1}{4}$ and $\frac{3}{4}$ are like fractions. To add and subtract like fractions, just add or subtract the numerators.

Example 1

Add. $\frac{5}{6} + \frac{3}{6}$

Add the numerators. Write the sum over the denominator.

$$\frac{5}{6} + \frac{3}{6} = \frac{5+3}{6} = \frac{8}{6}$$

Write the fraction in simplest form.

$$\frac{8}{6} = \frac{8 \div 2}{6 \div 2} = \frac{4}{3}$$

If the fraction is improper, write it as a mixed number.

$$\frac{4}{3} = 1\frac{1}{3}$$

$\frac{5}{6} + \frac{3}{6} = 1\frac{1}{3}$

Example 2

Subtract. $1\frac{3}{4} - \frac{3}{4}$

Write the mixed number as an improper fraction.

$$1\frac{3}{4} = \frac{1 \times 4}{1 \times 4} + \frac{3}{4}$$
$$= \frac{4}{4} + \frac{3}{4} = \frac{7}{4}$$

Subtract the numerators. Write the difference over the denominator.

$$\frac{7}{4} - \frac{3}{4} = \frac{7-3}{4} = \frac{4}{4}$$

Write the fraction in simplest form.

$$\frac{4}{4} = \frac{4 \div 4}{4 \div 4} = \frac{1}{1}, \text{ or } 1$$

$1\frac{3}{4} - \frac{3}{4} = 1$

DISCUSS

How would you find the sum of $\frac{3}{8}$ and $\frac{7}{8}$?

Guided Practice

Patrice has $2\frac{1}{8}$ yards of ribbon. She uses $\frac{5}{8}$ yard for a craft project. How much ribbon does she have left?

Step 1 Show the problem: $2\frac{1}{8} - \frac{5}{8}$

Write $2\frac{1}{8}$ as an improper fraction.

Write a fraction for the whole number by using the denominator, 8.

$$2\frac{1}{8} = \frac{2 \times 8}{1 \times 8} + \frac{1}{8}$$

Then find the sum of the fractions.

$$2\frac{1}{8} = \frac{16}{8} + \frac{1}{8} = \frac{17}{8}$$

$$2\frac{1}{8} = \frac{\square}{8}$$

Step 2 Subtract the numerators.
Write the difference over the denominator.

$$\frac{\square}{8} - \frac{5}{8} = \frac{\square}{8}$$

Step 3 Write the fraction in simplest form.

$$\frac{12}{8} = \frac{12 \div 4}{8 \div 4} = \frac{\square}{2}$$

THINK

To write a fraction in simplest form, divide the numerator and denominator by the same number.

Step 4 Write the improper fraction as a mixed number.

$$\frac{\square}{2} = \square\frac{\square}{2}$$

Patrice has __________ yards of ribbon left.

Independent Practice

1. How do you add or subtract like fractions?

____

____

2. Is the sum of $\frac{1}{4} + \frac{2}{4}$ less than or greater than 1? Explain.

____

____

Ask Yourself

Did I add or subtract the numerators only?

Did I write the answer in simplest form?

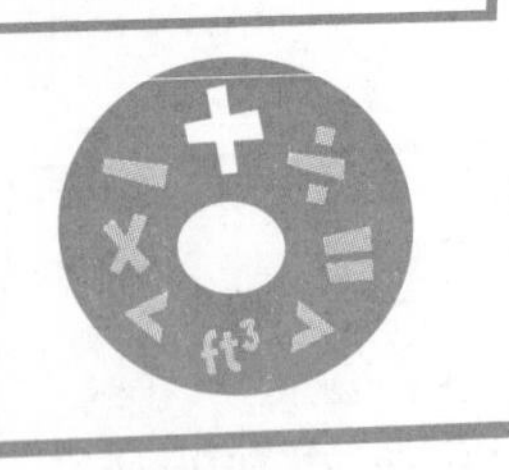

Find the sum or difference. Write it in simplest form.

3. $\frac{1}{8} + \frac{5}{8} = \frac{\square}{8} =$ ________

4. $\frac{5}{6} + \frac{4}{6} = \frac{\square}{6} =$ ________

5. $\frac{6}{8} - \frac{2}{8} = \frac{\square}{8} =$ ________

6. $\frac{12}{5} - \frac{7}{5} = \frac{\square}{5} =$ ________

7. To make punch, Ginny mixed $\frac{3}{4}$ quart lemonade and $\frac{3}{4}$ quart orange juice. How many quarts of punch did she make?

____

8. Ethan ate $\frac{3}{10}$ of a pizza and Mel ate $\frac{7}{10}$ of a pizza. How much more pizza did Mel eat than Ethan?

____

Find the sum or difference. Write it in simplest form.

9. $\frac{2}{3} + \frac{5}{3} =$ ________

10. $\frac{3}{4} + 2\frac{1}{4} =$ ________

11. $\frac{3}{8} + \frac{7}{8} =$ ________

12. $2\frac{1}{6} + 1\frac{3}{6} =$ ________

13. $1\frac{1}{6} - \frac{5}{6} =$ ________

14. $\frac{4}{5} - \frac{1}{5} =$ ________

15. $1\frac{1}{12} - \frac{9}{12} =$ ________

16. $\frac{11}{10} - \frac{5}{10} =$ ________

17. $\frac{2}{8} + \frac{7}{8} =$ ________

18. $4\frac{1}{2} - \frac{3}{2} =$ ________

19. $\frac{3}{5} + 1\frac{3}{5} =$ ________

20. $2\frac{5}{12} - \frac{11}{12} =$ ________

Solve each problem.

21. At the track meet, Karla's first long jump was $4\frac{1}{6}$ yards. Her second long jump was $3\frac{5}{6}$ yards. How much longer was her first jump than her second jump?

____

22. The basketball team practiced free throws for $\frac{3}{4}$ hour and lay-up shots for $\frac{1}{4}$ hour. Then they scrimmaged for $\frac{2}{4}$ hour. How long did the basketball team practice all together?

____

4 Add and Subtract Unlike Fractions

Key Words
common denominator
unlike fractions

When you add or subtract fractions, the fractions must have the same denominator. Fractions with different denominators are **unlike fractions**. Before you can add or subtract unlike fractions, you must write equivalent fractions so the fractions have a **common denominator**. One way to find a common, or same, denominator is to multiply the denominators.

Example

Renee is training for the swim team. On Monday, she swims $\frac{3}{4}$ mile. On Wednesday, she swims $\frac{1}{2}$ mile. How much farther does Renee swim on Monday than on Wednesday?

Show the problem: $\frac{3}{4} - \frac{1}{2}$

$\frac{3}{4}$ and $\frac{1}{2}$ are unlike fractions. Write equivalent fractions so they have the same denominator. Multiply the denominators to find a common denominator.

$4 \times 2 = 8$ 8 is a common denominator.

Use the common denominator to write equivalent fractions.

$\frac{3}{4} = \frac{3 \times 2}{4 \times 2} = \frac{6}{8}$ $\frac{1}{2} = \frac{1 \times 4}{2 \times 4} = \frac{4}{8}$

Then subtract.

$\frac{3}{4} - \frac{1}{2}$

↓ ↓

$\frac{6}{8} - \frac{4}{8} = \frac{2}{8}$

Write the difference in simplest form.

$\frac{2}{8} = \frac{2 \div 2}{8 \div 2} = \frac{1}{4}$

Renee swam $\frac{1}{4}$ mile farther on Monday than on Wednesday.

APPLY

Find a common denominator for the fractions $\frac{3}{8}$ and $\frac{1}{4}$. Explain your reasoning.

Guided Practice

To make salad dressing, Jacob mixed $\frac{2}{3}$ cup vinegar with $1\frac{1}{2}$ cups olive oil. How much salad dressing did he make?

Step 1 Show the problem: $\frac{2}{3} + 1\frac{1}{2}$
Write the mixed number as an improper fraction.

$1\frac{1}{2} = \frac{3}{2}$ so, $\frac{2}{3} + 1\frac{1}{2}$.

$$\frac{2}{3} + \frac{3}{2}$$

Step 2 Find a common denominator.

$3 \times 2 = 6$ ← common denominator

Step 3 Use the common denominator to write equivalent fractions.

$$\frac{2}{3} = \frac{2 \times 2}{3 \times 2} = \frac{\square}{6}$$

$$\frac{3}{2} = \frac{3 \times 3}{2 \times 3} = \frac{\square}{6}$$

REMEMBER
To write equivalent fractions, multiply the numerator and denominator by the same number.

Step 4 Add the fractions.

$$\frac{\square}{6} + \frac{\square}{6} = \frac{\square}{6}$$

THINK
Add the numerators only. The denominators stay the same.

Step 5 Write the improper fraction as a mixed number.

$$\frac{\square}{6} = 2\frac{\square}{6}$$

Jacob made _______ cups of salad dressing.

Independent Practice

1. What must you do *first* before adding or subtracting unlike fractions?

____

____

2. How can you find a common denominator for two unlike fractions?

____

____

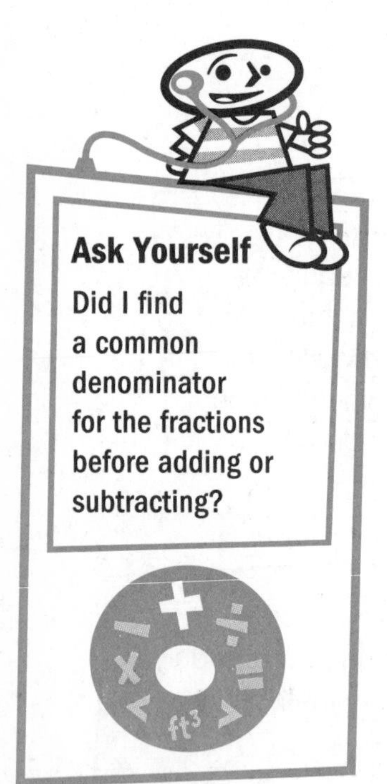

Find the sum or difference. Write it in simplest form.

3. $\frac{3}{8} + \frac{3}{4} =$ ________

4. $\frac{1}{3} + \frac{5}{6} =$ ________

5. $\frac{5}{2} - \frac{3}{4} =$ ________

6. $\frac{7}{3} - \frac{3}{2} =$ ________

7. In Mrs. Ananda's class, $\frac{1}{3}$ of the students have a dog as a pet and $\frac{1}{4}$ of the students have a cat as a pet. What fraction of the class has a cat or dog as a pet?

____

8. On Tuesday, Demarco walked $1\frac{1}{5}$ miles. On Wednesday, he walked $\frac{7}{10}$ mile. How much farther did Demarco walk on Tuesday than on Wednesday?

____

Find the sum or difference. Write it in simplest form.

9. $\frac{5}{6} + \frac{2}{3} =$ ______

10. $2\frac{1}{2} + 1\frac{3}{4} =$ ______

11. $\frac{4}{9} + \frac{1}{3} =$ ______

12. $1\frac{2}{3} - 1\frac{3}{6} =$ ______

13. $2\frac{1}{6} - \frac{1}{2} =$ ______

14. $3 - 2\frac{1}{5} =$ ______

15. $1 + \frac{3}{4} =$ ______

16. $\frac{6}{4} - \frac{2}{3} =$ ______

17. $\frac{3}{8} + 1\frac{1}{4} =$ ______

Solve each problem.

18. On Friday, Yolanda biked $3\frac{1}{5}$ miles. On Saturday, she biked $2\frac{3}{10}$ miles. How much farther did Yolanda bike on Friday than on Saturday?

______

19. A pie recipe calls for $3\frac{1}{2}$ cups blueberries and $1\frac{1}{4}$ cups peaches. How many cups of fruit are in the pie?

______

20. Lou says $\frac{3}{4} - \frac{1}{2} = \frac{2}{2} = 1$. Explain what he did wrong. Then write the correct answer.

______

______

5 Understanding Multiplication of Fractions

Key Words

product

To multiply a fraction by a fraction, multiply the numerators. Then multiply the denominators. Write the answer, the **product**, in simplest form.

When you multiply a given number by a fraction *less* than 1, the product is *less* than the given number.

When you multiply a given number by a fraction *greater* than 1, the product is *greater* than the given number.

Example 1

Predict. Is $\frac{1}{4} \times \frac{2}{3}$ less than or greater than $\frac{1}{4}$? Then multiply.

Think: $\frac{2}{3} < 1$, so the product of $\frac{1}{4} \times \frac{2}{3}$ is less than $\frac{1}{4}$.

Multiply the numerators. Then multiply the denominators.

$$\frac{1}{4} \times \frac{2}{3} = \frac{1 \times 2}{4 \times 3} = \frac{2}{12}$$

Write the product in simplest form.

$$\frac{2}{12} = \frac{2 \div 2}{12 \div 2} = \frac{1}{6}$$

$\frac{1}{4} \times \frac{2}{3} = \frac{1}{6}$ (Notice that the product, $\frac{1}{6}$, is less than $\frac{1}{4}$.)

Example 2

Predict. Is $\frac{1}{4} \times \frac{5}{3}$ less than or greater than $\frac{1}{4}$? Then multiply.

Think: $\frac{5}{3} > 1$, so the product of $\frac{1}{4} \times \frac{5}{3}$ is greater than $\frac{1}{4}$.

Multiply the numerators.
Then multiply the denominators.

$$\frac{1}{4} \times \frac{5}{3} = \frac{1 \times 5}{4 \times 3} = \frac{5}{12}$$

$\frac{1}{4} \times \frac{5}{3} = \frac{5}{12}$ (Notice that $\frac{5}{12} > \frac{1}{4}$.)

PREDICT

Is the product of $3 \times \frac{1}{2}$ less than or greater than 3? Explain your reasoning.

Guided Practice

Predict. Is the product of $\frac{3}{5} \times \frac{1}{3}$ less than or greater than $\frac{3}{5}$?
Then multiply to find the product.

Step 1 Compare $\frac{1}{3}$ to 1.

$\frac{1}{3} < 1$

So, the product must be ________ than $\frac{3}{5}$.

Step 2 Find the product.
Multiply the numerators. Then multiply the denominators.

$$\frac{3}{5} \times \frac{1}{3} = \frac{3 \times 1}{5 \times 3} = \frac{\square}{\square}$$

Step 3 Simplify.

$$\frac{3}{15} = \frac{3 \div 3}{15 \div 3} = \frac{\square}{\square}$$

Is the product less than or
greater than $\frac{3}{5}$? ________________

REMEMBER
To write a fraction in simplest form, divide the numerator and denominator by the same number.

$\frac{3}{5} \times \frac{1}{3} \bigcirc \frac{3}{5}$

$\frac{3}{5} \times \frac{1}{3} =$ ________

Independent Practice

1. How do you multiply two fractions?

____

____

2. Is the product of $\frac{1}{4} \times \frac{7}{6}$ less than or greater than $\frac{1}{4}$? Explain.

____

____

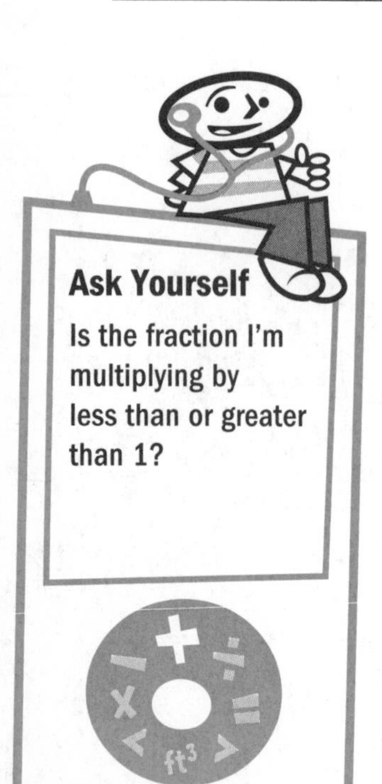

Compare. Write $<$ or $>$.

3. $\frac{1}{3} \times \frac{5}{8} \bigcirc \frac{1}{3}$

4. $\frac{3}{7} \times \frac{3}{2} \bigcirc \frac{3}{7}$

5. $\frac{5}{4} \times \frac{1}{2} \bigcirc \frac{5}{4}$

6. $\frac{4}{3} \times \frac{5}{3} \bigcirc \frac{4}{3}$

Use this information to solve questions 7 and 8.

Candace has $\frac{1}{2}$ of a sub sandwich left over. She eats $\frac{1}{3}$ of the left over sandwich.

7. Is the amount she eats greater than or less than $\frac{1}{2}$ of a sub sandwich?

   ____

8. How much of the left over sub sandwich does she eat?

   Multiply. $\frac{1}{2} \times \frac{1}{3} =$ ______________

Find the product. Write it in simplest form.

9. $\frac{1}{3} \times \frac{1}{4} =$ ______

10. $\frac{3}{4} \times \frac{1}{2} =$ ______

11. $\frac{7}{8} \times \frac{3}{2} =$ ______

12. $\frac{3}{7} \times \frac{2}{3} =$ ______

13. $\frac{5}{6} \times \frac{3}{4} =$ ______

14. $\frac{1}{8} \times \frac{4}{3} =$ ______

15. $\frac{3}{8} \times \frac{3}{2} =$ ______

16. $\frac{1}{4} \times \frac{3}{4} =$ ______

17. $\frac{4}{9} \times \frac{1}{3} =$ ______

18. $\frac{2}{3} \times \frac{5}{2} =$ ______

19. $\frac{5}{6} \times \frac{2}{1} =$ ______

20. $\frac{7}{8} \times \frac{3}{7} =$ ______

Solve each problem.

A baker bought $\frac{5}{2}$ pints of blueberries. He used $\frac{3}{4}$ of the blueberries to make tarts.

21. Did the baker use more than or less than $\frac{5}{2}$ pints?

______

22. How many pints of blueberries did the baker use?

Multiply. $\frac{5}{2} \times \frac{3}{4} =$ ______

6 Multiply Fractions

You can draw models to multiply fractions and whole numbers. Another way to multiply is to write the whole number as a fraction. Then multiply as you would two fractions.

Example 1

Ayana is making biscuits. The recipe calls for $\frac{3}{4}$ cup of milk. How many cups of milk does she need to make 2 batches of biscuits?

Use circles to show 2 groups of $\frac{3}{4}$.

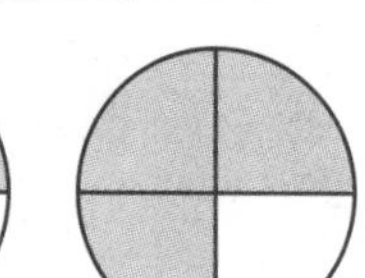

Count the shaded fourths.

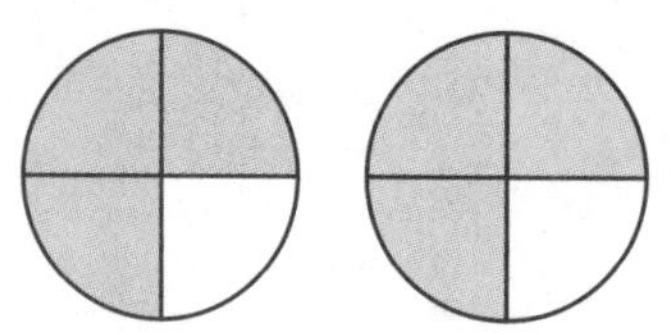

Write the answer as a mixed number.

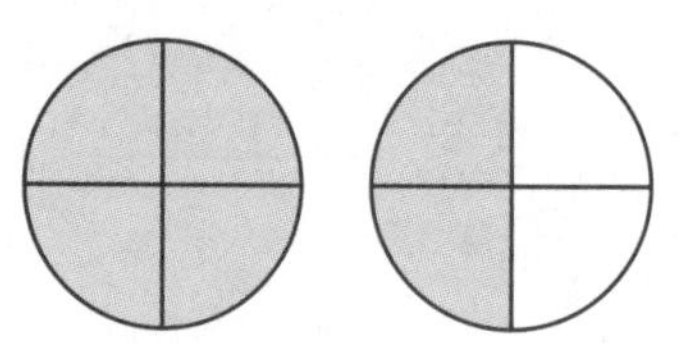

Ayana needs $1\frac{1}{2}$ cups of milk.

Example 2

Multiply. $4 \times \frac{5}{8}$

Write the whole number as a fraction with a denominator of 1.

$$4 = \frac{4}{1}$$

Multiply the numerators.
Then multiply the denominators.

$$\frac{4}{1} \times \frac{5}{8} = \frac{4 \times 5}{1 \times 8} = \frac{20}{8}$$

Write the product as a mixed number in simplest form.

$$\frac{20}{8} = 2\frac{4}{8} = 2\frac{1}{2}$$

$4 \times \frac{5}{8} = 2\frac{1}{2}$

DISCUSS

How can you write any whole number as a fraction? Give two examples of whole numbers written as fractions.

Guided Practice

Seung is making fruit punch for the class picnic. The recipe calls for $\frac{2}{3}$ pint of strawberries. How many pints of strawberries does he need to make 4 batches of punch?

Step 1 Show the problem: $4 \times \frac{2}{3}$

Write the whole number as a fraction.

$4 = \frac{\square}{1}$

THINK

$\frac{4}{1}$ means the same as $4 \div 1$.

So, $\frac{4}{1} = 4 \div 1 = 4$.

Step 2 Multiply the numerators.
Then multiply the denominators.

$\frac{4}{1} \times \frac{2}{3} = \frac{4 \times 2}{1 \times 3} = \frac{\square}{\square}$

REMEMBER

To write an improper fraction as a mixed number, divide the numerator by the denominator.

$3\overline{)8}$ = 2 R2

Step 3 Write the improper fraction as a mixed number.

$\frac{\square}{\square} = \square\frac{\square}{3}$

Step 4 Use models to check your answer.
Show 4 groups of $\frac{2}{3}$.
Count the shaded thirds.

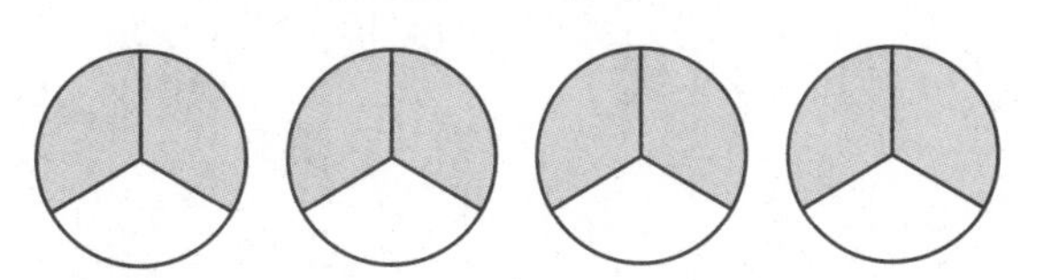

There are ________ thirds shaded.

Step 5 Write the answer as a mixed number.

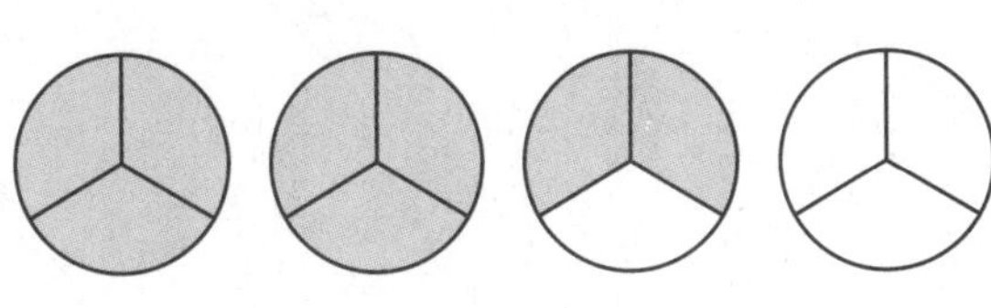

____

Seung needs ____________________ pints of strawberries.

Independent Practice

1. How can you use a model to multiply a whole number by a fraction?

____

____

2. How can you use multiplication to multiply a whole number by a fraction?

____

____

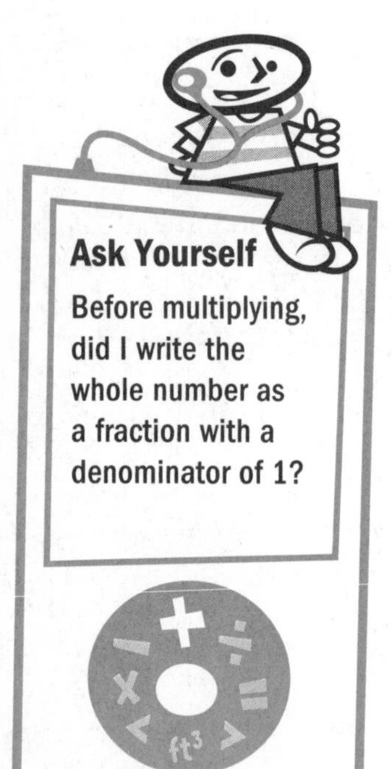

Draw a model to find the product.

3. $3 \times \frac{1}{4} =$ ________

4. $4 \times \frac{2}{5} =$ ________

Multiply.

5. $7 \times \frac{1}{2} =$ ________

6. $5 \times \frac{2}{3} =$ ________

7. Celio is making 4 batches of apple-date bars. He needs $\frac{1}{3}$ cup vegetable oil for each batch. How much vegetable oil does he need?

____

8. Lauren made 5 pitchers of lemonade. Each pitcher holds $\frac{1}{2}$ gallon of lemonade. How much lemonade did she make?

____

Find the product. Write it in simplest form.

9. $5 \times \frac{3}{4} =$ ________

10. $6 \times \frac{1}{3} =$ ________

11. $\frac{1}{5} \times 7 =$ ________

12. $6 \times \frac{3}{4} =$ ________

13. $\frac{2}{5} \times 8 =$ ________

14. $8 \times \frac{3}{4} =$ ________

15. $10 \times \frac{3}{7} =$ ________

16. $\frac{1}{3} \times 15 =$ ________

17. $\frac{3}{8} \times 12 =$ ________

18. $3 \times \frac{2}{3} =$ ________

19. $\frac{2}{3} \times 11 =$ ________

20. $8 \times \frac{5}{6} =$ ________

Solve each problem.

21. Dan is making 2 batches of chicken soup. Each batch of soup uses $\frac{2}{3}$ cup of rice. How many cups of rice does he need?

____

22. For the school musical, Leila needs 10 ribbons that are each $\frac{3}{4}$ yard long. She has a spool of ribbon that holds 8 yards of ribbon. Does Leila have enough ribbon? Explain.

____

____

7 Fractions as Division

A fraction is another way to show division. You can interpret a fraction as division of the numerator by the denominator. The fraction $\frac{3}{4}$ is the same as 3 divided by 4.

$$\frac{3}{4} = 3 \div 4$$

You can use this relationship to divide a whole number into equal groups.

Example

Five friends want to split 3 pizzas evenly. How should they divide the pizzas so that each gets the same number of slices?

Show the problem: $3 \div 5$

You can use fraction strips to model 3 divided by 5.

Show 3 whole fraction strips.

Then show each whole divided into fifths.

Divide the fifths into 5 equal groups.

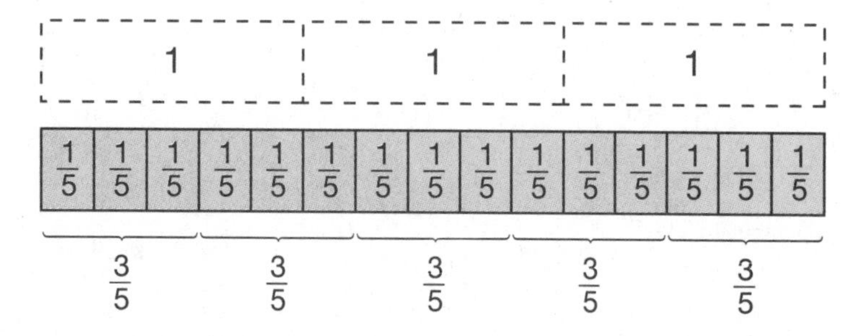

The model shows that $3 \div 5$ is equal to $\frac{3}{5}$.

Use multiplication to check that $3 \div 5 = \frac{3}{5}$. Multiply the divisor by the quotient.

$$\frac{3}{5} \times 5 = \frac{3}{5} \times \frac{5}{1} = \frac{3 \times 5}{5 \times 1} = \frac{15}{5} = 3$$

Each friend gets $\frac{3}{5}$ of a pizza.

DEMONSTRATE

How would you use fraction strips to show $3 \div 4$?

Guided Practice

Two campers want to split 3 gallons of water evenly. How many gallons of water will each camper get?

Step 1 Use fraction strips to show the problem: $3 \div 2$.

Use 3 whole strips. Then show each whole divided into halves. Divide the halves into 2 equal groups.

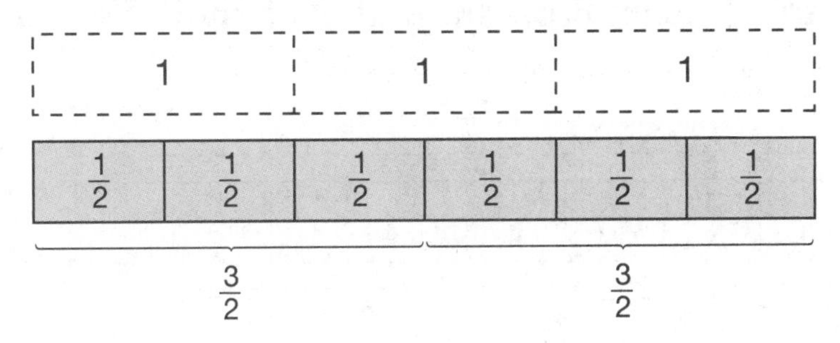

$3 \div 2 = \frac{\square}{\square}$

Step 2 Multiply to check that $3 \div 2 = \frac{3}{2}$.

$\frac{3}{2} \times 2 = \frac{\square}{2} \times \frac{2}{\square} = \frac{\square \times 2}{2 \times \square} = \frac{\square}{2} = 3$

Step 3 The answer is an improper fraction.

Write the answer as a mixed number.

$\frac{3}{2} = \square\frac{1}{\square}$

REMEMBER
To write an improper fraction as a mixed number, divide the numerator by the denominator.

Each camper gets _________ gallons of water.

Independent Practice

1. How can you write a fraction as a division problem?

____

____

Write the division problem that each model represents.

2.

1				1			
$\frac{1}{4}$	$\frac{1}{4}$	$\frac{1}{4}$	$\frac{1}{4}$	$\frac{1}{4}$	$\frac{1}{4}$	$\frac{1}{4}$	$\frac{1}{4}$

$\frac{2}{4}$ $\frac{2}{4}$ $\frac{2}{4}$ $\frac{2}{4}$

____

3.

1						1						1					
$\frac{1}{6}$	$\frac{1}{6}$	$\frac{1}{6}$	$\frac{1}{6}$	$\frac{1}{6}$	$\frac{1}{6}$	$\frac{1}{6}$	$\frac{1}{6}$	$\frac{1}{6}$	$\frac{1}{6}$	$\frac{1}{6}$	$\frac{1}{6}$	$\frac{1}{6}$	$\frac{1}{6}$	$\frac{1}{6}$	$\frac{1}{6}$	$\frac{1}{6}$	$\frac{1}{6}$

$\frac{3}{6}$ $\frac{3}{6}$ $\frac{3}{6}$ $\frac{3}{6}$ $\frac{3}{6}$ $\frac{3}{6}$

____

4. Seven campers divide 8 gallons of water evenly. How many gallons of water does each camper receive?

____

Write each fraction as a division problem.

5. $\frac{7}{10}$ = ________ 6. $\frac{3}{8}$ = ________ 7. $\frac{6}{5}$ = ________

8. $\frac{2}{3}$ = ________ 9. $\frac{7}{3}$ = ________ 10. $\frac{9}{5}$ = ________

Write each division as a fraction or a mixed number. Write the answer in simplest form.

11. $5 \div 6$ = ________ 12. $8 \div 12$ = ________ 13. $9 \div 6$ = ________

14. $20 \div 4$ = ________ 15. $12 \div 9$ = ________ 16. $7 \div 8$ = ________

17. $5 \div 10$ = ________ 18. $28 \div 6$ = ________ 19. $30 \div 8$ = ________

Solve each problem.

20. Brianna divides a 5-pound bag of peanuts into 8 bags to sell at the school fair. If each bag weighs the same amount, how many pounds of peanuts are in each bag?

____

21. Ten people want to split 6 bushels of apples evenly. How many bushels will each person receive?

____

22. Nine people want to split a 20-pound bag of rice evenly. How many pounds of rice will each person receive? Between which two whole numbers does your answer lie?

____

8 Divide with Fractions

Key Words

reciprocals
unit fraction

You can use fraction strips to divide a whole number by a unit fraction. A **unit fraction** is a fraction with a numerator of 1.

Another way to divide a whole number by a fraction is to multiply the whole number times the **reciprocal** of the fraction. Reciprocals are two numbers that have a product of one. To find the reciprocal, switch the numerator and the denominator of the divisor. The reciprocal of $\frac{1}{4}$ is $\frac{4}{1}$ since $\frac{1}{4} \times \frac{4}{1} = 1$.

Example

A road crew paves $\frac{1}{4}$ mile of road each day. How many days will it take the crew to pave 2 miles?

Show the problem: $2 \div \frac{1}{4}$

Use fraction strips. Show 2 whole fraction strips.

Then show each whole divided into fourths.

1				1			
$\frac{1}{4}$	$\frac{1}{4}$	$\frac{1}{4}$	$\frac{1}{4}$	$\frac{1}{4}$	$\frac{1}{4}$	$\frac{1}{4}$	$\frac{1}{4}$

Count the $\frac{1}{4}$ strips.

There are 8 strips.

$$2 \div \frac{1}{4} = 8$$

Use reciprocals to find $2 \div \frac{1}{4}$.

Multiply the reciprocal of $\frac{1}{4}$.

$$2 \div \frac{1}{4} = 2 \times \frac{4}{1}$$

$$= 2 \times 4$$

$$= 8$$

It will take the road crew 8 days.

APPLY

How would you find $7 \div \frac{1}{8}$?

Guided Practice

1 Divide. $3 \div \frac{1}{8}$

Step 1 Find the reciprocal of $\frac{1}{8}$.

The reciprocal of $\frac{1}{8}$ is $\frac{8}{1}$, or ________.

Step 2 Multiply the whole number times the reciprocal.

$3 \div \frac{1}{8} = 3 \times$ ________

$=$ ________

$3 \div \frac{1}{8} =$ ________

THINK

To write the reciprocal of a fraction, "flip" the numerator and denominator. So, the reciprocal of $\frac{1}{8}$ is $\frac{8}{1}$, or 8.

2 Divide. $\frac{1}{8} \div 6$

Step 1 Find the reciprocal of 6.

The reciprocal of $\frac{6}{1}$ is $\frac{1}{\square}$.

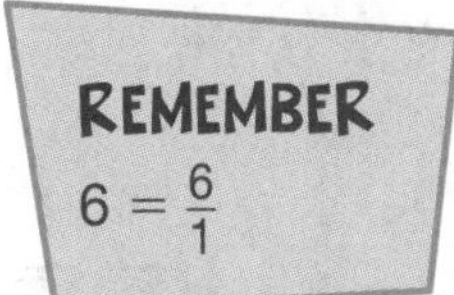

REMEMBER

$6 = \frac{6}{1}$

Step 2 Multiply the fraction times the reciprocal.

$\frac{1}{8} \div 6 = \frac{1}{8} \times \frac{1}{\square}$

$=$ ________

$\frac{1}{8} \div 6 =$ ________

Independent Practice

1. How can you divide a whole number by a fraction?

____

____

2. How can you divide a fraction by a whole number?

____

____

Ask Yourself

Did I write the reciprocal of the fraction or whole number before multiplying?

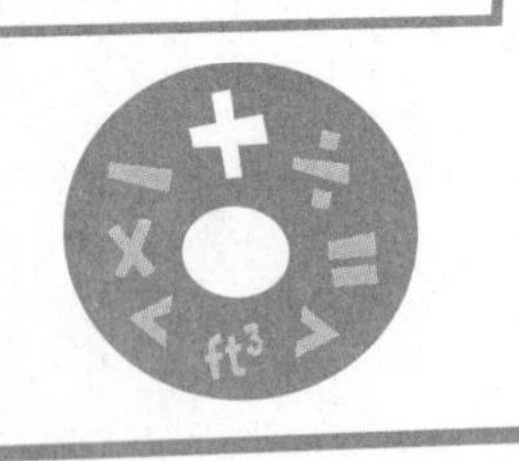

Write the reciprocal of each number.

3. 7 ________ 4. $\frac{1}{3}$ ________ 5. $\frac{1}{10}$ ________

6. $\frac{1}{5}$ ________ 7. 8 ________ 8. $\frac{1}{6}$ ________

Use reciprocals to divide.

9. $2 \div \frac{1}{5} = 2 \times \frac{5}{1}$
$= 2 \times \square$
$=$ ________

10. $4 \div \frac{1}{6} = 4 \times \frac{6}{1}$
$= 4 \times \square$
$=$ ________

11. $\frac{1}{5} \div 4 = \frac{1}{5} \times \frac{1}{\square}$
$=$ ________

12. $\frac{1}{8} \div 8 = \frac{1}{8} \times \frac{1}{\square}$
$=$ ________

13. Four hikers divide $\frac{1}{2}$ gallon of water evenly. How much water does each hiker receive?

____

Divide. Write the answer in simplest form.

14. $8 \div \frac{1}{6} =$ ______

15. $\frac{1}{9} \div 10 =$ ______

16. $4 \div \frac{1}{8} =$ ______

17. $\frac{1}{2} \div 5 =$ ______

18. $20 \div \frac{1}{4} =$ ______

19. $\frac{1}{7} \div 8 =$ ______

20. $10 \div \frac{1}{3} =$ ______

21. $\frac{1}{8} \div 2 =$ ______

22. $1 \div \frac{1}{2} =$ ______

23. $\frac{1}{12} \div 3 =$ ______

24. $9 \div \frac{1}{4} =$ ______

25. $\frac{1}{5} \div 5 =$ ______

Solve each problem.

26. Three friends divide $\frac{1}{2}$ of a pizza evenly. How much pizza does each friend get?

______

27. Shanti is making lunches for her family. She wants to put a $\frac{1}{3}$-cup serving of raisins in each lunch. How many servings of raisins can she make with 2 cups of raisins?

______

Glossary

common denominator a common multiple of two or more denominators (Page 16)

equivalent fractions fractions that name the same amount (Page 4)

Example: $\frac{1}{2}$ and $\frac{2}{4}$ are equivalent fractions.

fraction names part of a whole or a group (Page 4)

Example: $\frac{3}{8}$

improper fraction a fraction in which the numerator is greater than the denominator (Page 8)

Example: $9 \div 5$

like fractions fractions that have the same denominator (Page 12)

mixed number a number made up of a whole number part and a fraction part (Page 8)

Example: $4\frac{1}{3}$

product the answer to a multiplication problem (Page 20)

reciprocals two numbers that have a product of 1 (Page 32)

Example: 6 and $\frac{1}{6}$ are reciprocals because $6 \times \frac{1}{6} = 1$.

unit fraction a fraction with a numerator of 1 (Page 32)

unlike fractions fractions that have different denominators (Page 16)

Math Tools: Number Lines

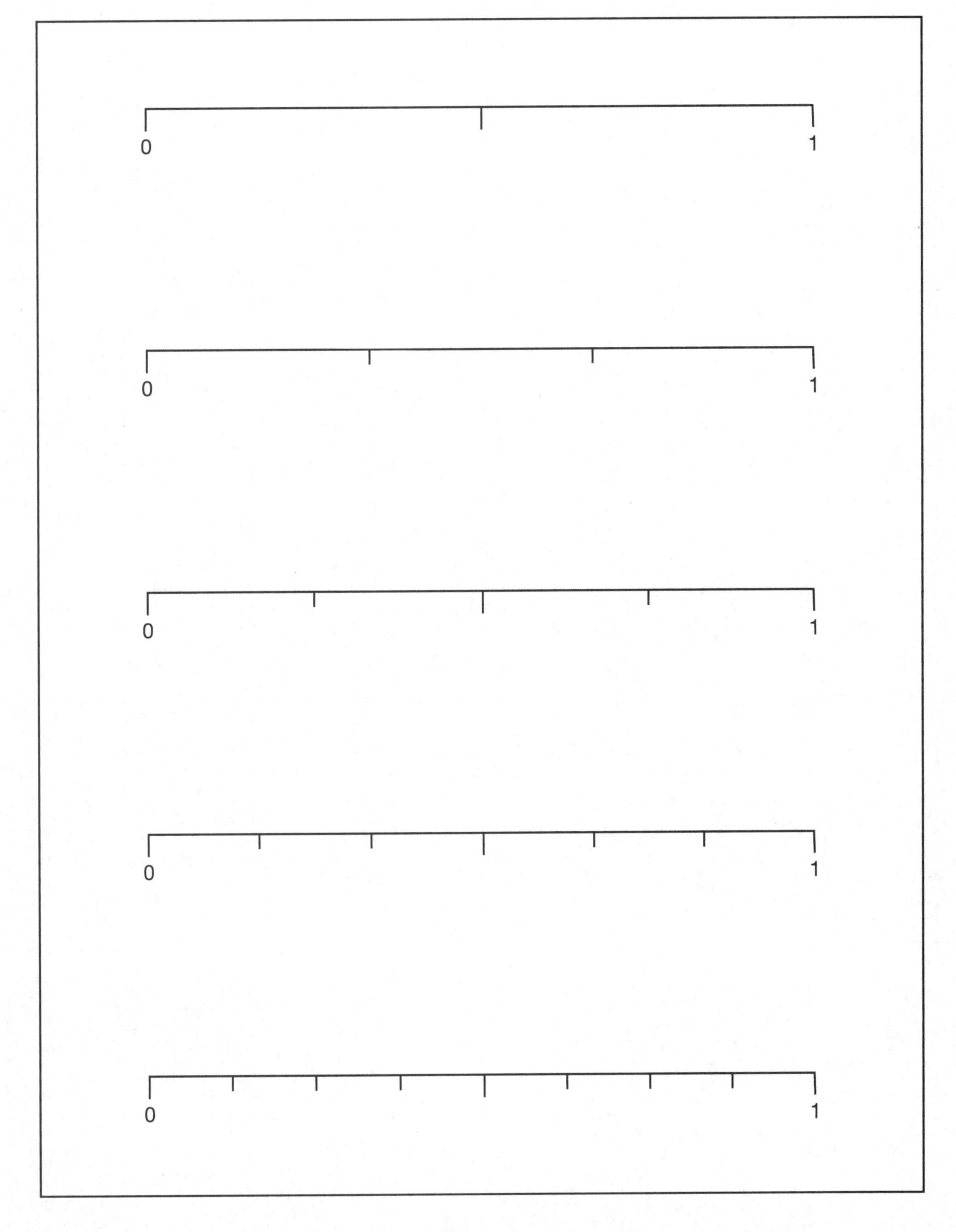

Math Tools: Fraction Models

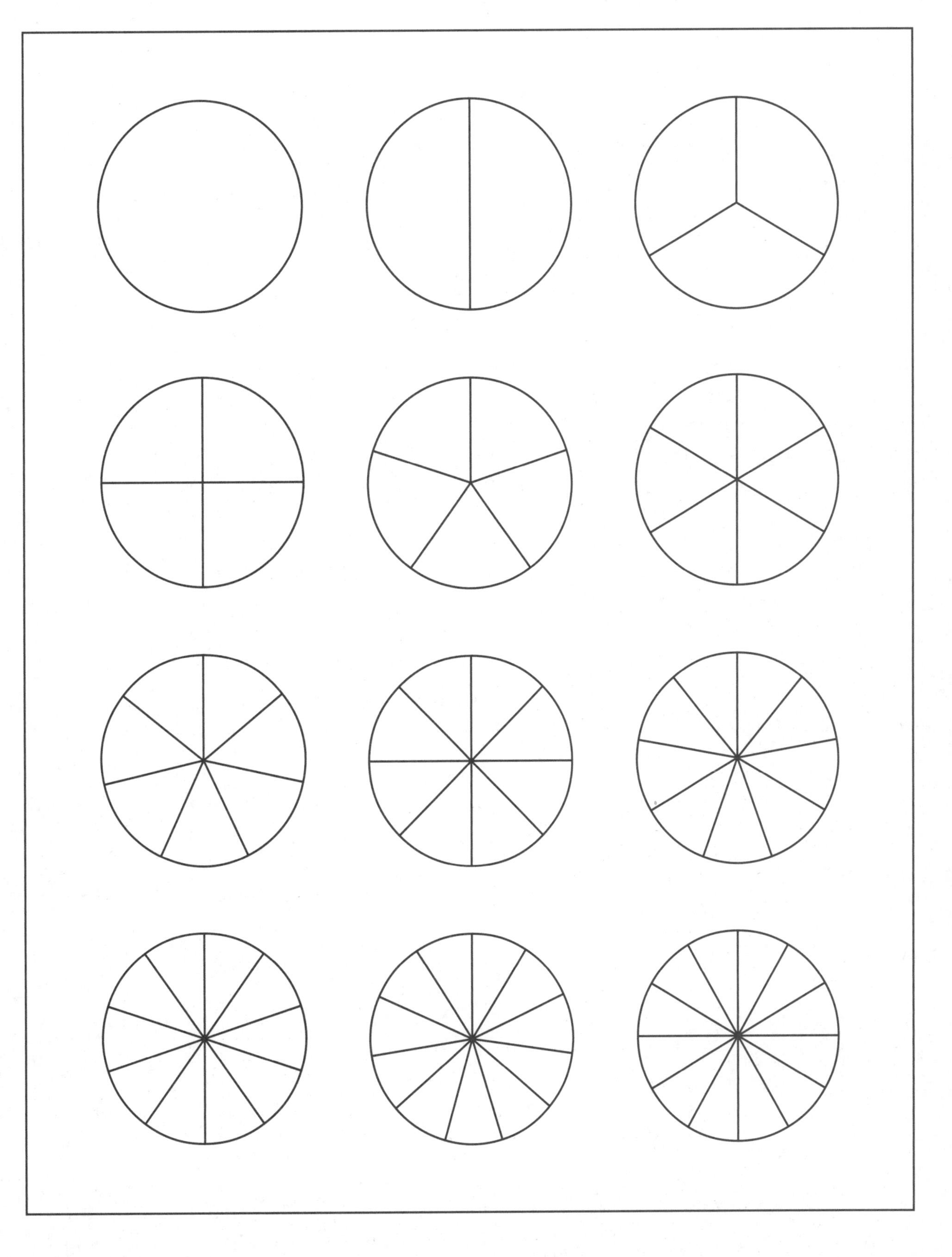

Cut or tear carefully along this line.